The author lives in Seattle and is fortunate to have a wonderful kind-hearted wife who is instrumental in his involvement in animal welfare organizations and projects. They have fostered countless dogs over many years. Of course they couldn't help but adopt a few them.

EVA

Jack Hirsch

AUSTIN MACAULEY PUBLISHERS™
· LONDON · CAMBRIDGE · NEW YORK · SHARJAH ·

Copyright © Jack Hirsch (2019)

Ordering Information:
Quantity sales: special discounts are available on quantity purchases by corporations, associations, and others. For details, contact the publisher at the address below.

Publisher's Cataloging-in-Publication data
Hirsch, Jack
Eva

ISBN 9781643784014 (Paperback)
ISBN 9781643784021 (Hardback)
ISBN 9781645367703 (ePub e-book)

The main category of the book — JUVENILE FICTION / Animals / Dogs

www.austinmacauley.com/us

First Published (2019)
Austin Macauley Publishers LLC
40 Wall Street, 28th Floor
New York, NY 10005
USA

mail-usa@austinmacauley.com
+1 (646) 5125767

Dedicated to the animal shelters and rescue organizations of the world who help lost and abandoned animals.

Eva's story was made possible by the tireless efforts of SOI Dog in Phuket Thailand whose goal is to care for homeless and injured dogs; and my wife, Melinda, who adopted Eva.

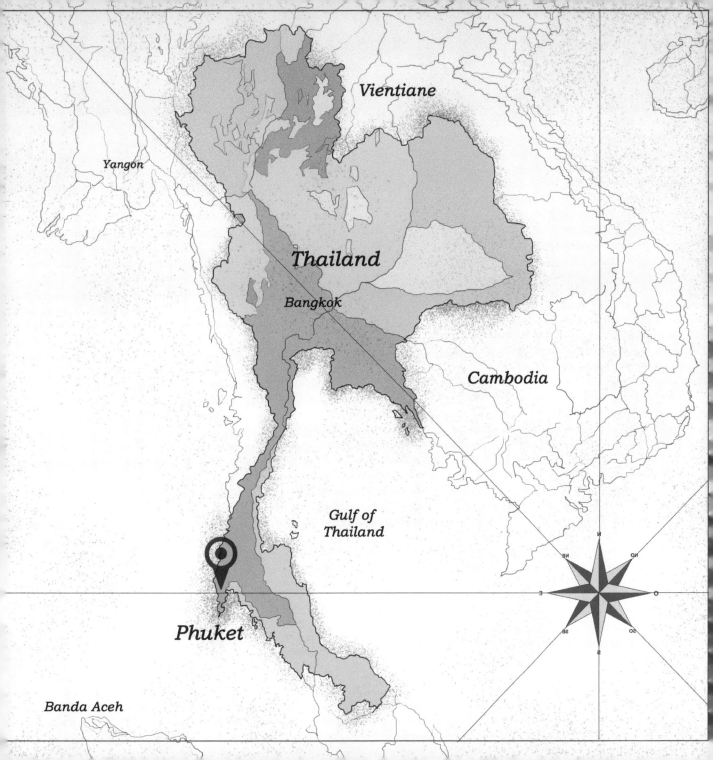

My name is Eva. I am a dog. I am old and only have three legs, but I wasn't always like this.

I want to tell you the story of my life. All living things have a story and this is mine. Sometimes it's happy and sometimes sad, but that is the way life is. Now, I have a wonderful home with a people-family who care for me, dog friends, good food, and a soft bed for my sore back leg.

I was born in Phuket, Thailand. To me, it was just where I was born. My mommy was beautiful. She was black with big ears that had furry edges. I think I look like her. I knew her by her smell and when I think back, I can still remember it. I had brothers and sisters, and knew them by smell too. Mommy had found us a crate behind a restaurant to live in where she kept us warm and safe, and fed us. She taught us many lessons on how to find food and to tell who was friendly or mean by their sound and smell. She told us to stay away from big, fast moving things that could hurt us. This was a good time in my life.

As I got bigger, I didn't see my mommy or brothers and sisters as much. That was sad but I used her lessons to find a place to live and food to eat. Some people were nice and gave me food, and some were mean and chased me. Other dogs would chase me too. Then I had to find new places to live. The days were mostly the same and some were good and some bad, but I am smart and found ways to get by. Sometimes I would see my mommy or brothers and sisters, but they were busy. I miss not having them as family any more. This is the way I lived for a long time. I had people-friends, who liked me and I tried to be around them as much as I could, but I didn't have a real house.

One day, I smelled some good food and was trying to get to it, but was hit by one of the big, fast things and my back leg was hurt real bad and wouldn't work to move me. I curled up and waited to die, but someone picked me up and took me to a place where they helped me and tried to save my leg. They were so kind and tried really hard, but it didn't work and that is how I only have one back leg.

They gave me a name, Eva, and good food. There were many people and dogs and I got to recognize some, but all were good to me, even the dogs. I lived there in what they called a shelter for two years. It was a good time and I was safe. I learned to get around with only three legs.

One day, I was given a special meal and some of the people were sad. They said I was going on a trip to a real house. I thought I was in a real house now. I went into a large box that was like the box I was born in, but it was scary because I was alone. I seemed sleepy most of the time but still really afraid. I remember loud noises and bumps where I felt sick. It lasted forever and nothing smelled right.

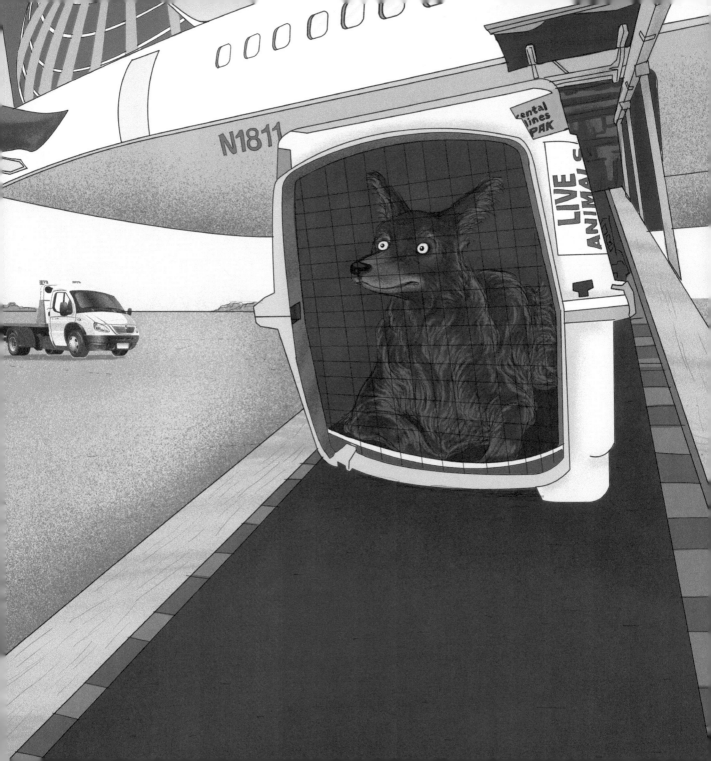

When it all stopped, I was in a strange place and could hear people, and smell some other dogs that smelled afraid too. Two people opened the door to my box. They smelled friendly and petted me but everything was different. I still had to be afraid.

We went to a place where I smelled other dogs and went inside a house. I had never been in a house. It was warm and smelled good. I got food. There were three other dogs who seemed nice but they were bigger than me. I was worried and wanted them to stay away. After a while, I could tell they wouldn't hurt me and one of them stayed with me to help me.

The people are very good to me. I am safe here and can finally not be afraid any more. I have my own places to eat and sleep. I can't get up stairs but my people help by lifting my bottom and give me treats when I get to the top. I try really hard to learn all the ways of the house, like when we eat and to go outside with the others to potty. I am very happy here. The happiest I have been in my life. My people tell me this is my forever-house and I don't have to find another one, ever.

I am Eva and I have told you my story. I am tired now and need to sleep.

CPSIA information can be obtained
at www.ICGtesting.com
Printed in the USA
LVHW070014300719
625828LV00012B/887/P